Compiled and edited by Arthur Dick.

The Complete Blues Guitar Player: Book 1

Exclusive Distributors:
Music Sales Limited, 8/9 Frith Street, London W1V 5TZ, England.
Music Sales Pty Limited, 120 Rothschild Avenue, Rosebery, NSW 2018, Aus

Order No. AM91083
ISBN 0-7119-3414-2
This book © Copyright 1993 by Wise Publications

GW00730096

Book design by Studio Twenty, London
Computer management by Adam Hay Editorial Design
Cover photography by Julian Hawkins

Music processed by The Pitts

Printed in the United Kingdom by
J.B. Offset Printers (Marks Tey) Limited, Marks Tey, Essex.

Your Guarantee of Quality
As publishers, we strive to produce every book to the highest commercial standards. The music has been freshly engraved and the book has been carefully designed to minimise awkward page turns and to make playing from it a real pleasure. Particular care has been given to specifying acid-free, neutral-sized paper made from pulps which have not been elemental chlorine bleached. This pulp is from farmed sustainable forests and was produced with special regard for the environment. Throughout, the printing and binding have been planned to ensure a sturdy, attractive publication which should give years of enjoyment. If your copy fails to meet our high standards, please inform us and we will gladly replace it.

Music Sales' complete catalogue lists thousands of titles and is free from your local music shop, or direct from Music Sales Limited. Please send a cheque/postal order for £1.50 for postage to: Music Sales Limited, Newmarket Road, Bury St. Edmunds, Suffolk IP33 3YB.

Wise Publications
London/New York/Paris/Sydney/Copenhagen/Madrid

Tablature & Instructions Explained

The tablature stave comprises six lines, each representing a string on the guitar as illustrated.

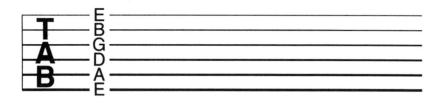

A number on any of the lines indicates, therefore, the string and fret on which a note should be played.

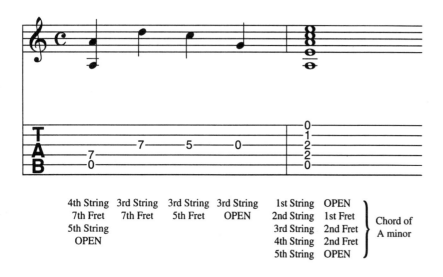

4th String	3rd String	3rd String	3rd String	1st String	OPEN	
7th Fret	7th Fret	5th Fret	OPEN	2nd String	1st Fret	
5th String				3rd String	2nd Fret	Chord of
OPEN				4th String	2nd Fret	A minor
				5th String	OPEN	

A useful hint to help you read tablature is to cut out small squares of self-adhesive paper and stick them on the upper edge of the guitar neck adjacent to each of the frets, numbering them accordingly. Be careful to use paper that will not damage the finish on your guitar.

Finger Vibrato

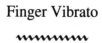

Tremolo Arm Vibrato

Glissando

Strike the note, then slide the finger up or down the fretboard as indicated.

Tremolo Strumming

This sign indicates fast up and down stroke strumming.

8va

This sign indicates that the notes are to be played an octave higher than written.

loco

This instruction cancels the above.

This note-head indicates the string is to be totally muted to produce a percussive effect.

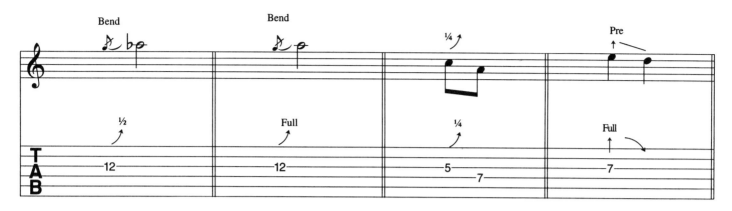

HALF TONE BEND

Play the note G then bend the string so that the pitch rises by a half tone (semi-tone).

FULL TONE BEND

DECORATIVE BEND

PRE-BEND

Bend the string as indicated, strike the string and release.

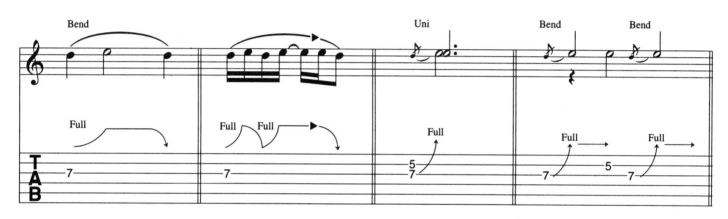

BEND & RELEASE

Strike the string, bend it as indicated, then release the bend whilst it is still sounding.

BEND & RESTRIKE

Strike the string, bend or gliss as indicated, then restrike the string where the symbol occurs.

UNISON BEND

Strike both strings simultaneously then immediately bend the lower string as indicated.

STAGGERED UNISON BEND

Strike the lower string and bend as indicated; whilst it is still sounding strike the higher string.

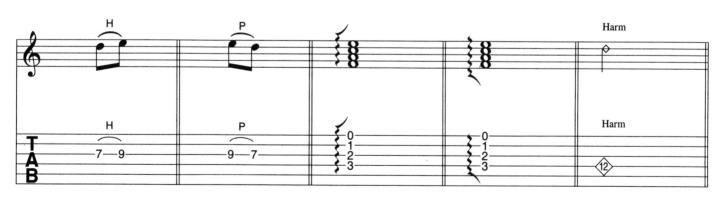

HAMMER-ON

Hammer a finger down on the next note without striking the string again.

PULL-OFF

Pull your finger off the string with a plucking motion to sound the next note without striking the string again.

RAKE-UP

Strum the notes upwards in the manner of an arpeggio.

RAKE-DOWN

Strum the notes downwards in the manner of an arpeggio.

HARMONICS

Strike the string whilst touching it lightly at the fret position shown. Artificial Harmonics, (A.H.), will be described in context.

The Blues

What makes a great blues solo? Is it the melody line, the phrasing, or the bending and vibrato attached to the notes? A knowledge of your scales is an obvious advantage, so too is the ability to turn the scales into useful phrases. Beyond this your technique has to be able to deliver the goods, but how you do this is up to you. Each player has his or her own statement to make and an individual voice with which to make it.

The beginning of this book deals with the most commonly used scales. It is important that you become familiar with using scales, as the following music examples show how they are used by famous blues players. If you are unsure which scale is which, always refer back to this section.

The analysis of these great players' ideas provides a valuable insight and inspiration for you to learn from. Blues playing, however, is heartfelt and emotive music. It goes beyond the actual notes played, and relies heavily on the more expressive techniques such as bends and vibratos to get the true 'feel'.

There is no substitute for listening to the real greats, learning from their skills and then applying them to your own playing. The musical extracts in this book are taken from available recordings, so read the music and, above all - listen!

To begin with let's look at some of the theory behind the blues. We will look at two vital areas

- The chord progressions and chord types that are used

- The scales which match these chords and progressions

This is all the basic information you will need to be able to play the blues. Armed with this we will be able to explore some of the classic blues riffs and phrases.

Classic Blues Progressions - The Twelve Bar And Eight Bar Blues

The blues sequence commonly falls into a twelve bar pattern, though a smaller eight bar version is also widely used.

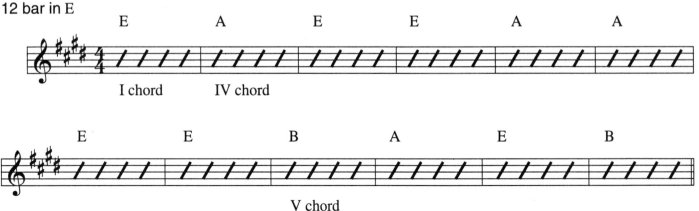

8 bar in E

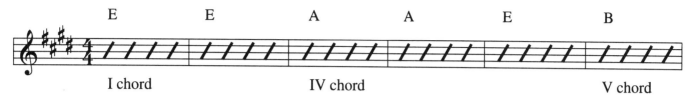

There are seven different notes in the major scale (in the scale of E these notes are E, F♯, G♯, A, B, C♯, and D♯). These degrees of the scale can be numbered I – VII, and their respective chords given these numbers. For example, in the key of E, chord IV is the chord of A. You don't need a degree in nuclear physics to work out that, by using numbers instead of names, we can easily transpose this system into other keys.

In the key of C (whose scale is made up of all the white notes on the piano C, D, E, F, G, A, and B) the fourth degree of the scale is the note F, so chord IV in the key of C is the chord of F. A word of warning: the chords in a major scale are made up of different chord types – a blend of major (strong) chords, minor chords (weak) and a diminished chord on the seventh degree. You don't need to know why this is, as long as you are aware of the different types.

The chords built on all major scales conform to this pattern

Scale	I	II	III	IV	V	VI	VII*
Chord type	Major	Minor	Minor	Major	Major	Minor	Diminished

* In the blues the seventh degree of the scale (and therefore its chord) is flattened to take away the sharp edges of the music. The flattened 7th is the most common 'blue' note and, as such is generally taken as read when talking about sevenths.

In the above examples the relationship between chords I, IV and V is the same, consequently most riffs and phrases will work in both. Let's stick to using the twelve bar sequence as a vehicle for our ideas; we'll assume that these ideas will work equally well over the shorter eight bar pattern.

As we've already found out, one of the primary characteristics of the blues sound is the flattened 7th. We can add flattened 7ths to all the chords in the progression to give them a 'bluesy' feel. These are so common that they are referred to as just '7ths', not minor or flattened 7ths.

There are many variants on the blues, though the most common version is as follows:

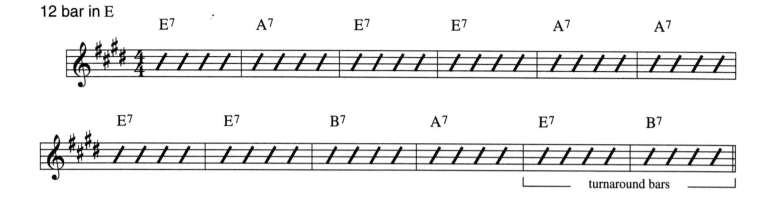

12 bar in E

The two turnaround bars act as a means of taking the piece back to its beginning and, as you will see, there are various permutations of chords available in these two bars (especially in jazz chord progressions or 'changes'). Similarly, we can use the turnaround bars as an introduction to a twelve bar.

Before moving on to single line scales and phrases it is important that you understand the rhythm of the blues style. The 'Blues Shuffle' is so called because of the feel of the groove. On many charts this is notated by ♪♩ = ♩♪ above the first bar, which is an indication that the rhythms should be played with a swinging, or shuffle style.

A typical twelve bar rhythm accompaniment might be played using the 4th, 5th and 6th strings. Use the palm of your right hand (pick hand) to damp the strings, creating a more precise and controlled rhythm.

We have already seen that the simplest turnaround consists of chord V going to chord I, and these can be decorated in a blues style by adding 7ths to the chords. We can further decorate the turnaround by inserting chord IV, thus, in E, the progression changes to:

E⁷ / A⁷ / E⁷ / B⁷ / :‖

or add chromatic movement to get to the V7 chord:

E⁷ / A⁷ / E⁷ A⁷ A♯⁷ B⁷ :‖

More 'Blue Notes'

The key of E has four sharps in its key signature*. However, the characteristic 7th flavour of the blues dictates that we should modify the scale accordingly.

This is where we start to explore the world of modes. Make sure you know all your major and minor scales before getting into this – it will make your life much easier in the long run!

This is in fact the Mixolydian mode, and is equivalent to playing A major, starting on the Vth degree of the scale.

Although this mode provides the flattened 7th there is another important blue note which we will need, and this is the flattened 3rd.

This is equivalent to beginning on the second degree of the D major scale. It is in fact the E Dorian mode. Against an E7 chord in our sequence this mode works very well.

Although major and minor scale types will work, they do not lend themselves to the Chicago, Delta or Texas blues styles, as the scales used in these styles are derived from jazz. So, instead of the major, minor and modal systems we use other scales. For the blues in E they are

Fig. 1. E major pentatonic

Fig. 2. E minor pentatonic

Fig. 3. E minor blues

* Sometimes the key signature is omitted when discussing a blues to avoid the continuous use of accidentals.

The Major Pentatonics

The primary chords available from the harmonised major scale are the chords I, IV and V, so we can employ the A and B major pentatonics as well. The D major scale (E Dorian, remember) generates another useful pentatonic. Check out the following:

Play the above pentatonic lines against an E7 chord – you will notice that they each create different and interesting colours against the same chord. All these examples are good, though the E major pentatonic scale is the 'bluesiest', and therefore most commonly used.

The Minor Pentatonics

Like the preceding major scales, E minor pentatonic is also a five note scale, though this time the flattened 3rd and 7th are both present. This provides an even more 'bluesy' feel. As you will probably notice, many blues phrases use minor pentatonics, or a combination of major and minor pentatonics.

Minor chords II, III and VI (F#m, G#m and C#m in the key of E) can also provide pentatonic alternatives.

I major pentatonic	has the same notes as	**VI minor pentatonic**.
Emaj (E, F♯, G♯, B, C♯)		C♯min (C♯, E, F♯, G♯, B)
IV major pentatonic	has the same notes as	**II minor pentatonic**
Amaj (A, B, C♯, E, F♯)		F♯min (F♯, A, B, C♯, E)
V major pentatonic	has the same notes as	**III minor pentatonic**
Bmaj (B, C♯, D♯, F♯, G♯)		G♯min (G♯, B, C♯, D♯, F♯)

You will notice that we are really seeing the use of related chords within the E major 'orbit'. The most commonly used major pentatonic for the blues in E is the E major pentatonic; this also applies to its relative minor (C♯ minor).

We have already seen that the E minor pentatonic, by virtue of its flattened 3rd and flattened 7th, creates the most 'bluesy' sound.

We can now add the final colour to our musical palette by including perhaps the 'bluesiest' note of all – the flattened 5th. By adding this note to the minor pentatonic we get a six note scale, which will open the door to a wealth of blues licks.

Em pentatonic

Em blues

This scale is called the **Minor Blues Scale**.

As you will have gathered by now, similar blues scales can be created from our other minor pentatonics (F♯m, G♯m and C♯m).

Even though the flattened 5th is not normally associated with the major scale, it is such a strong and emotive sound that your ear will readily accept it. In exactly the same way as the addition of the flattened 5th to the minor pentatonic forms the minor blues scale, so the same process with the major pentatonic gives us the **Major Blues Scale.**

E pentatonic

E blues

For the time being let's simplify matters by concentrating on the minor pentatonic and the minor blues scales. This doesn't mean we will disregard the major scales – you should always be aware of the relationship between the major and minor forms of the scale.

From what we have learned so far we can see that, for a blues in E, the following scales are most commonly used:

- Em pentatonic

- Em blues

- C♯m pentatonic (same as E pentatonic)

- C♯m blues (same as E Blues)

Let's now take a look at the positions on the fretboard where these scales are played. You will see that each scale forms a pattern over the fretboard; you will quickly learn these finger patterns, making it easier to use these scales when constructing blues phrases, and when transposing into new keys. By adapting these finger patterns you can work other scales into your licks.

Here are the basic scales for the blues in E:

Em pentatonic

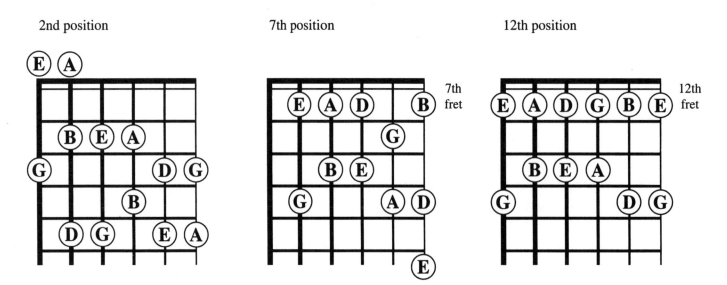

Em blues

Open position   7th position   12th position

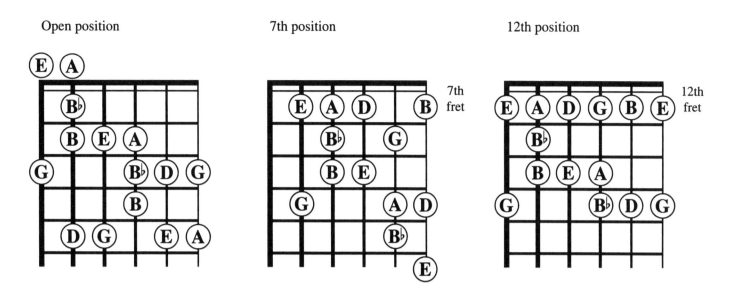

C#m pentatonic

4th position   9th position   11th position

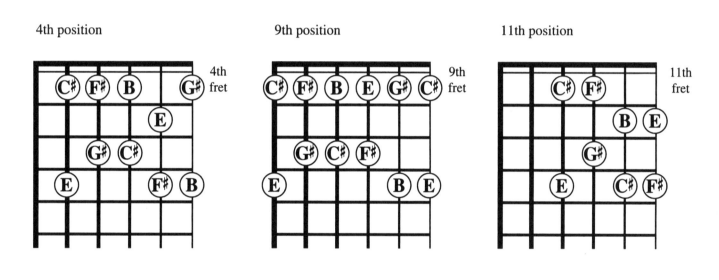

C#m blues

4th position   9th position   11th position

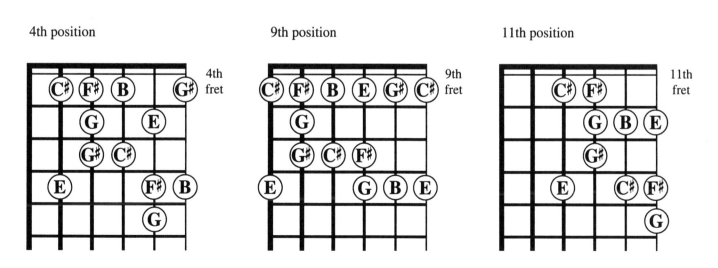

Many blues phrases will involve not just one scale, but fragments from several. Take one position on the fretboard and get used to playing the scales one after another, mixing them up. You will need to become as familiar as possible with them so that, when you learn a new phrase, you will understand where it comes from. More crucially, you will be able to take riffs and phrases and work them in to other scales and other keys. These scale shapes will form the foundation of your ability to express yourself in the blues. Spend some time on this stuff – it's important! Learn these scales well or you will pay the price later in frustration for yourself and predictably boring playing for the musicians you play with.

Now go back to the blues on page 6. The scales we have been looking at relate to chord I (or I7), but what about chords IV and V?

The Em pentatonic and blues scales can be played over all the changes in the progression. The major (and relative minor) pentatonic and blues scales can also be used for chords IV (A/F#m scales) and V (B/G#m scales).

Further options are available, for example the Mixolydian and Dorian modes work well. Use A Mixolydian and A Dorian over the A7 chord and B Mixolydian and B Dorian over the B7 chord.

As you look at the following solos you must always bear in mind the blues style. This is achieved with a combination of special techniques such as vibratos and bends. As you listen to more blues guitar you will pick up a sense of style which is common to all players, and then some quirks of style which are peculiar to certain individual artists. It's up to you to take what you want from what's out there.

Remember to experiment with all the phrases you learn – the key to good musicianship is flexibility, so try out as many variations as you can. Try transposing the riffs into different keys, or playing them at different octaves. You may experiment with tempo, feel, or groove, to evoke different moods and colours with the music.

Above all – have fun!

Crossroads
Eric Clapton

CD 'The Cream Of Eric Clapton'
Polydor 833 519 – 2

Words & Music by Robert Johnson
Arranged by Eric Clapton

The opening riffs in A and D are played in the open position. The notes within the phrases should be allowed to sustain i.e. let ring to varying amounts. Note the classic blues phrases in the turnaround bars played in the 5th position. Throughout the verse, the A riff and D riff are restated after each vocal line as per the blues sequence.

The opening of the solo is played around F♯m blues at the 2nd position up to the 5th position using some interesting double stops in bar 3. From bar 5 (chord IV) the Am pentatonic is used. Note the use of the bends and vibrato and how the bends and glissandi join the phrases together.

There are some great lines right through to the turnaround, which is similar to the turnaround phrase in the intro.

1st solo

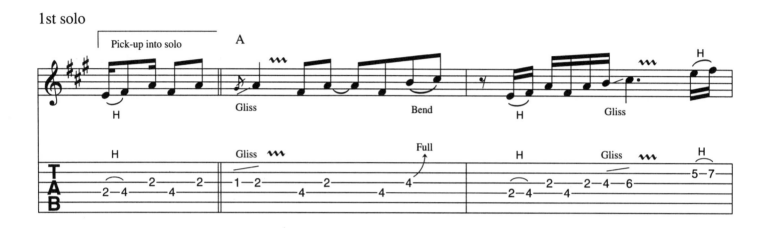

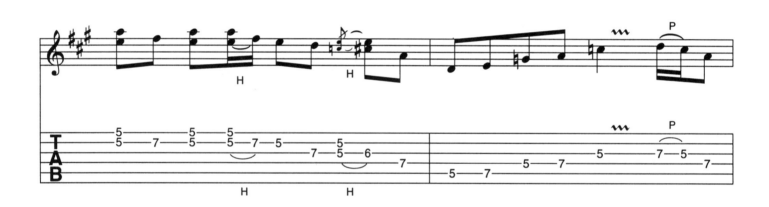

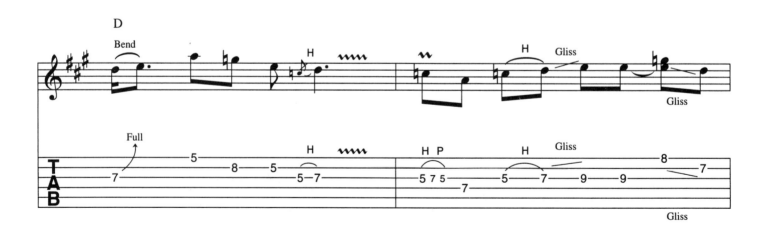

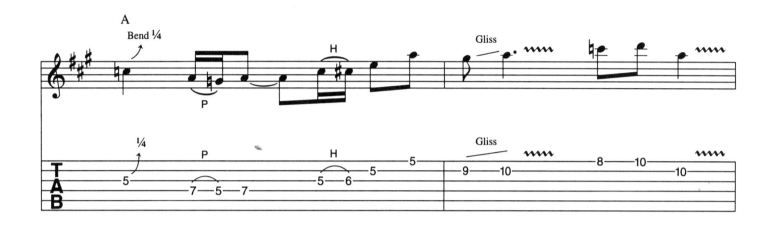

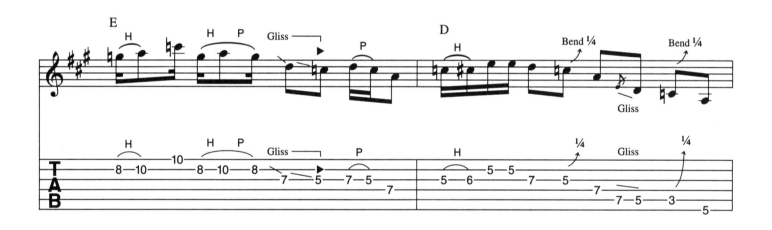

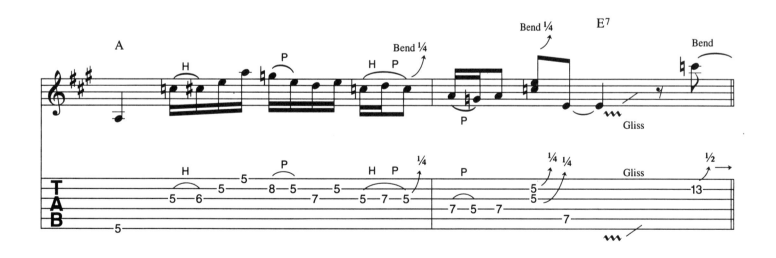

Into the next chorus we're up to the 10th position. The tension and edge of Clapton's playing is partially given by the expressive vibrato as in the 1st bar. The blues scale continues to be explored with double stops being used in bars 3,4 and 8. Note the sliding between positions to connect the fingering patterns. e.g. bars 8 to 9 and 9 to 10.

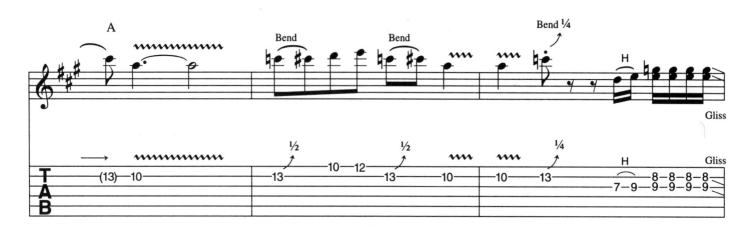

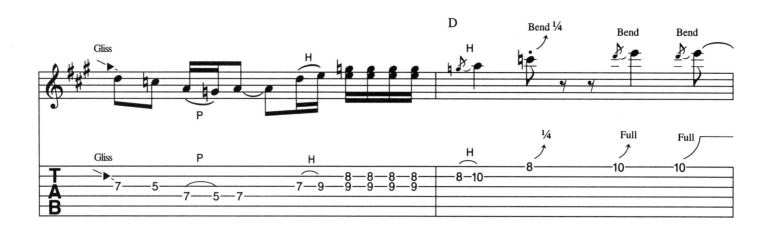

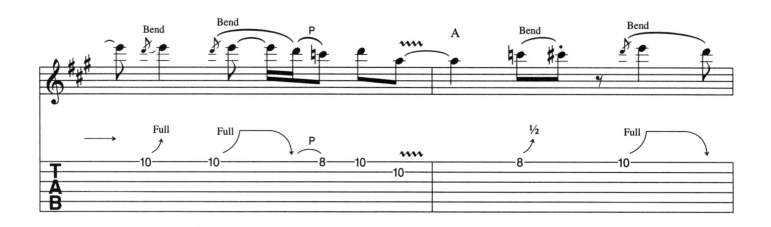

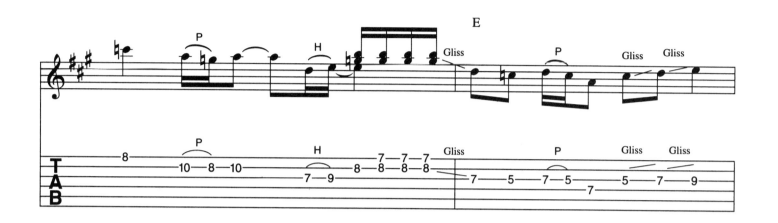

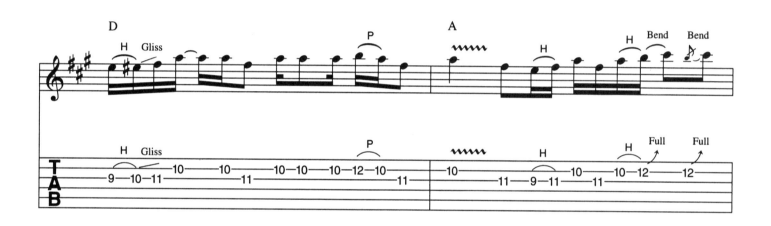

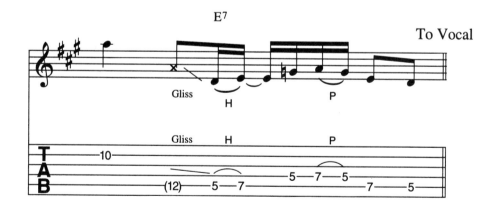

Sweet Little Angel

Buddy Guy

CD 'My Time After Awhile'
Vanguard VCD – 141/142

Words & Music by B.B. King & J. Taub

Buddy Guy's phrasing in slower tempos looks a little tricky when it's written down. Don't be put off though – it's not as difficult as it looks. Although the piece is written in $\frac{12}{8}$, the rhythm is generated by an extremely slow $\frac{4}{4}$ pulse of four beats per bar, each equivalent to three quavers. So one bar of $\frac{12}{8}$ can be subdivided into four bars of $\frac{3}{8}$. Working through the following examples will make this clear.

Example 1

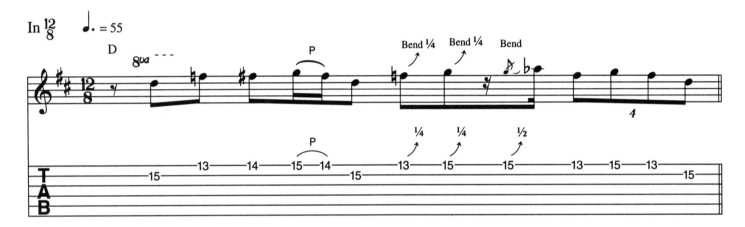

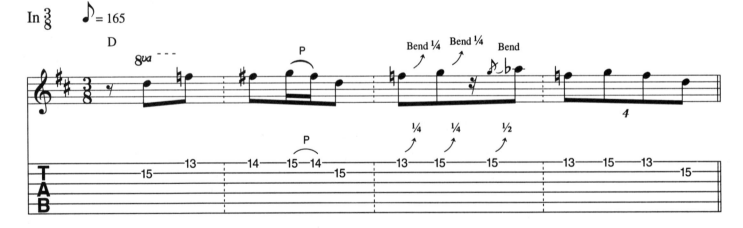

18

Example 2

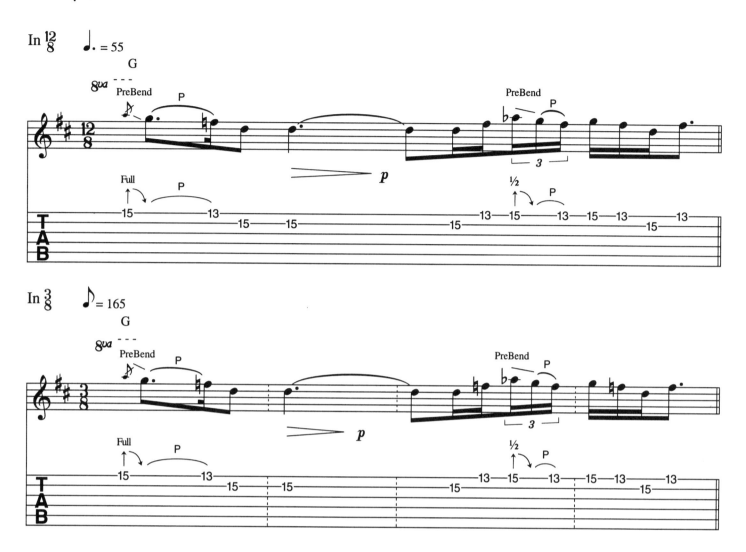

The following chorus is the intro to 'Sweet Little Angel' and shows off Buddy's phrasing and choice of notes. Played around the 10th and 13th fret positions he plays some great phrases based on the Dm blues scale. In bar 2 and bar 11 the F and F♯ run together i.e. the minor and major 3rd which gives it a jazzy flavour. The use of ¼ tone bends adds a real edge to the sound. The phrase on the 3rd beat of the 2nd bar uses the ¼ tone bend for the first two notes then a semitone bend for the last.

In bar 5 he uses different degrees of pre-bends within one phrase. The first is a tone, the second a semitone. The phrase is played delicately with no vibrato. Bars 8 and 9 are played at the 10th fret, note his choice of notes over the phrase leading up to the G7 in bar 10. Buddy has a very lyrical style with clean bends and little vibrato which gives him his unique sound.

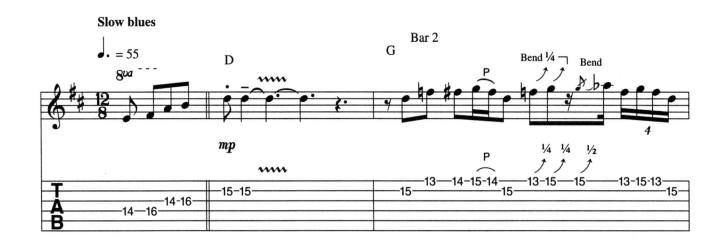

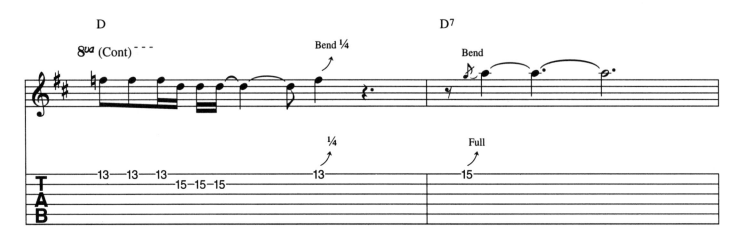

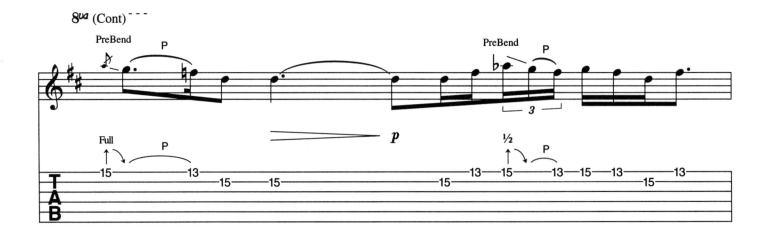

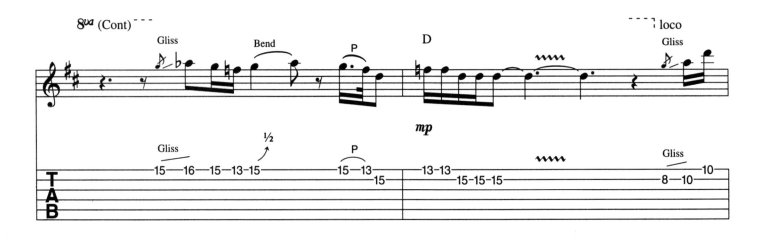

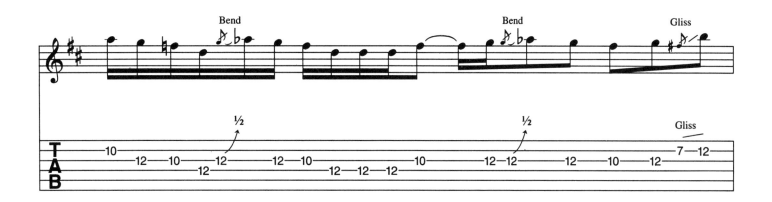

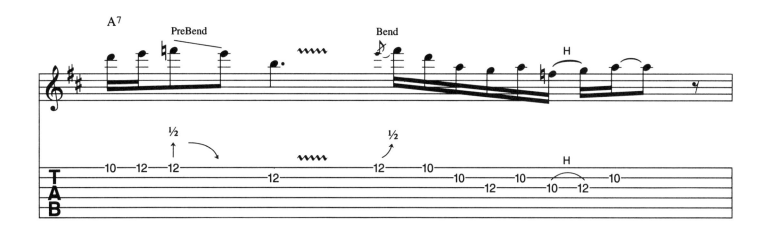

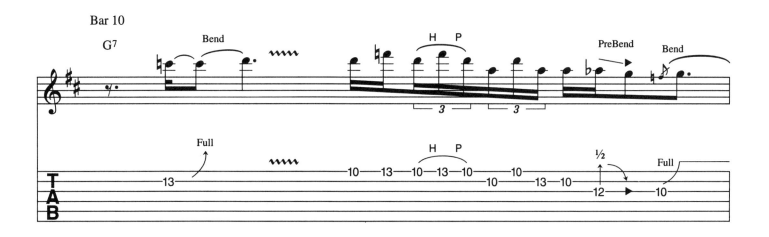

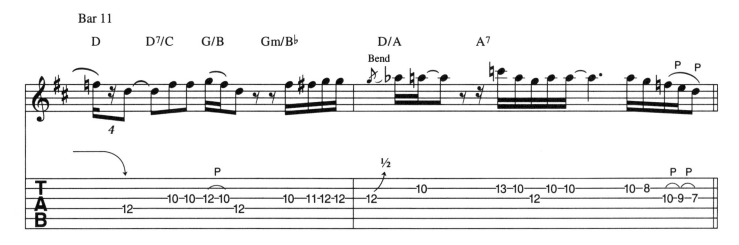

Rock My Plimsoul
Jeff Beck

LP 'Truth'
EMI SCX 6293

Words & Music by Rod Stewart & Jeff Beck

The following riff is played over a B chord. Transpose it accordingly to fit the E and F#7 chords of the twelve bar sequence. Using a slight overdriven sound, it should be played by damping the strings with the palm of your pick hand. This is a classic blues/rock line – try experimenting with it by varying the phrasing.

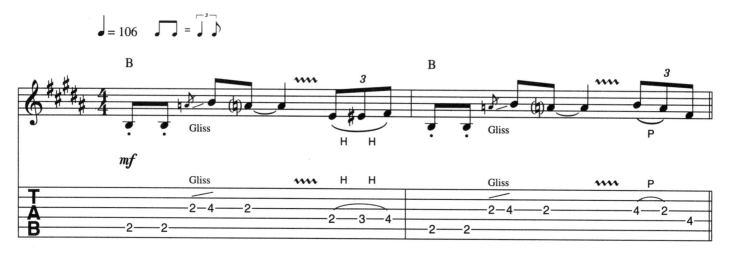

Jeff varies the riff by exploring other ideas under the vocal line. It should be played in a bottleneck/slide style.

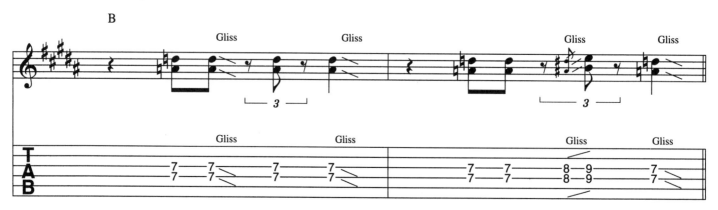

The following 24 bar solo shows off many of Jeff's playing characteristics. The opening unibends are very powerful and the double stopped bends in bar 4 are typical of his playing in this period. Note the phrases in bars 6 and 7 can be split into two parts. The first phrase in bar 6 carries on to beat two of bar 7 into bar 8. They are based on the Bm pentatonic and fall under the fingers even though the phrasing is a little tricky. The repetitive triplet in bars 9 and 10 leads to the double stopped phrase in bars 11 and 12. This has to be played accurately – pay special attention to your intonation. Jeff continues this effect into the next chorus [B] where, at the 3rd bar, he uses the bottleneck to give the slide effect but reverts to regular fingering for other phrases.

The repetitive motif is used over bars 7 and 8 with the bottleneck and with a trill over 9 and 10. He varied the speed of the trill across these bars which gives an interesting effect. The final top E he plays is beyond the usual fretboard range and is not given a fret location.

Solo

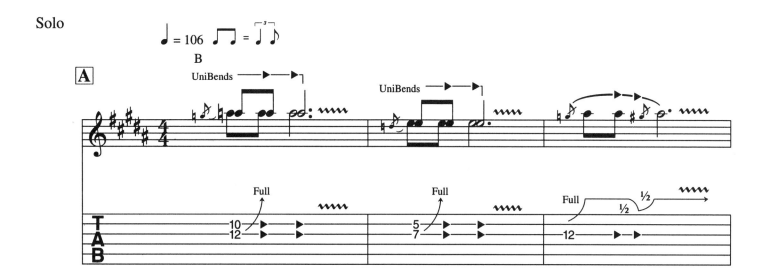

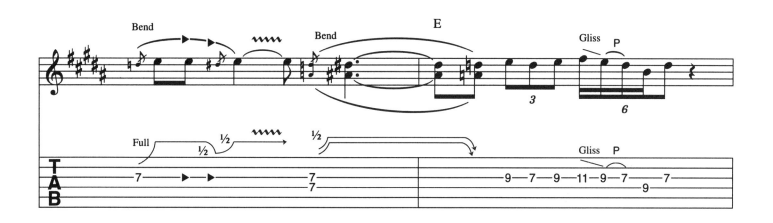

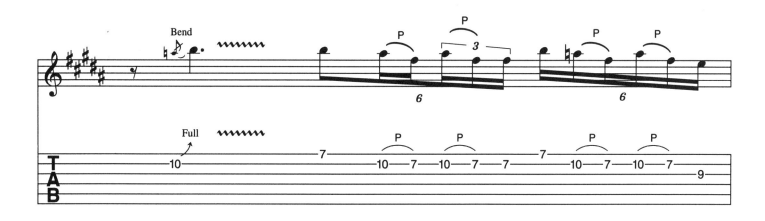

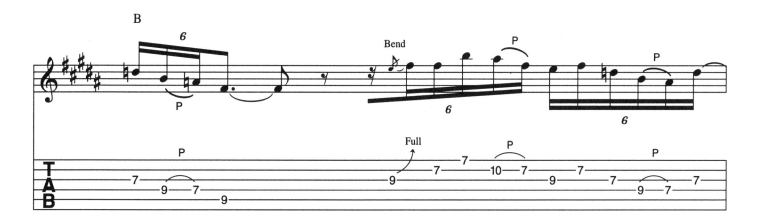

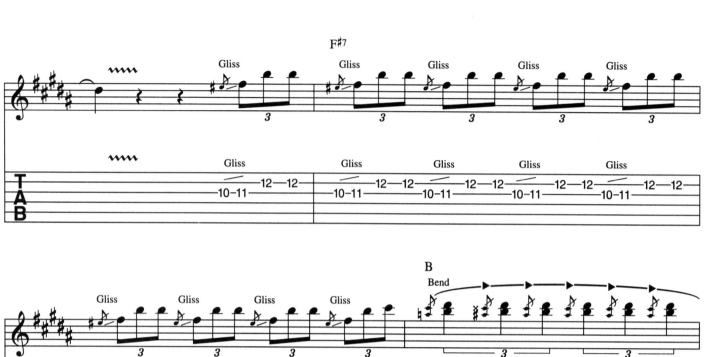

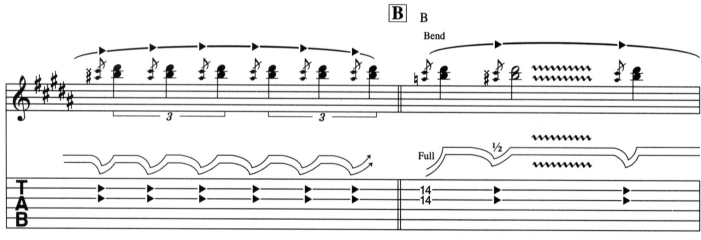

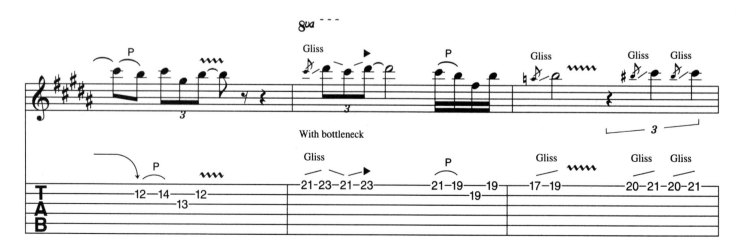

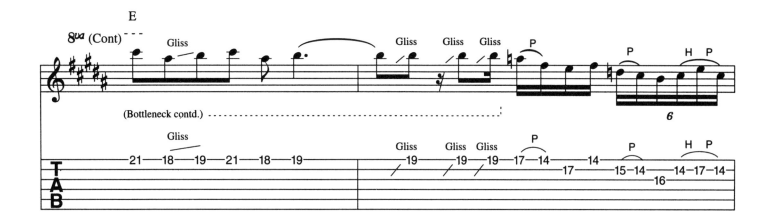

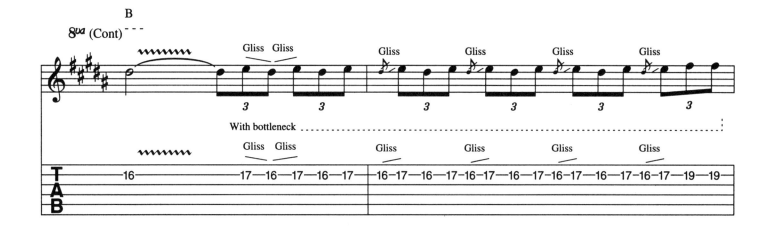

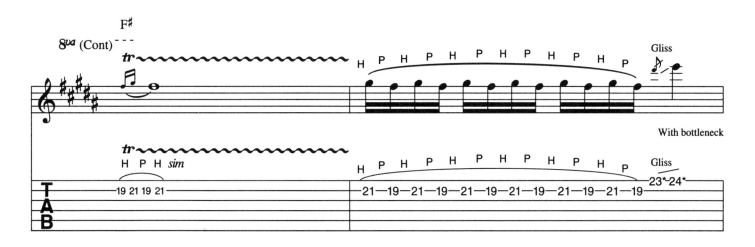

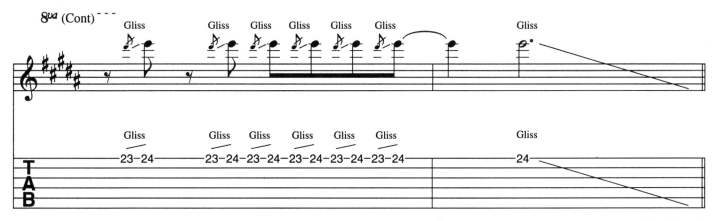

*Bottleneck can be played above the range of the fretboard.

Change It
Stevie Ray Vaughan

CD 'Soul To Soul'
Epic 466330 2

Words & Music by Doyle Bramhall

The power of Stevie's playing can be heard clearly in this piece. The opening pre-bend and vibrato in bar 1 and the 1½ tone bend in bar 2 typify his style. To improve the sound of the guitar and facilitate these bends his guitar is tuned a semitone down. So in fact, although he was playing A, on the guitar it sounded as A♭.

Intro

The following riffs are played under the vocal for the verses

The opening bars of the solo are similar to the intro in style. Note the 2 tone bend in the first bar – the bend is gradual across the third beat giving a very powerful feel. Most of the solo is played around the 8th position using the Am pentatonic scale. Stevie uses repetition to bring out the emotion – look at bars 6 and 8. His use of bends and vibrato with the repeating idea is very evocative.

Solo

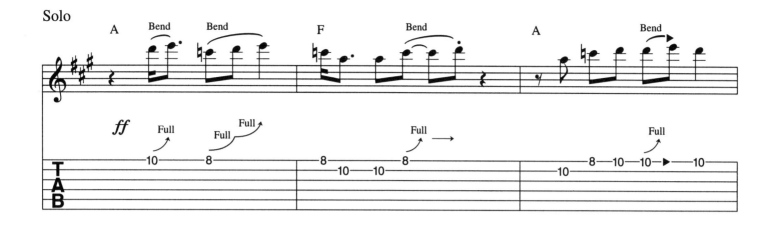

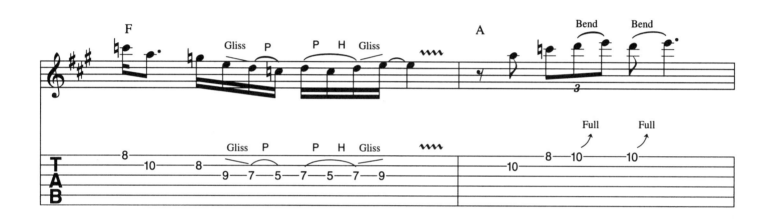

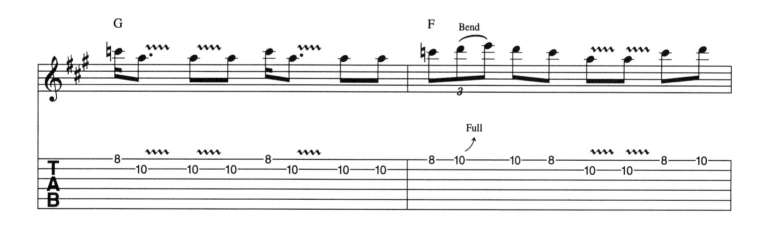

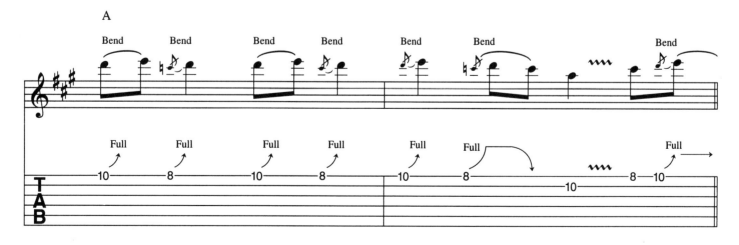

Although not a blues sequence, the nine bar pattern allows Stevie to play some great blues. In this second section look how he bends the double stops e.g. bars 4 and 5, and of special note across 5 into 6.

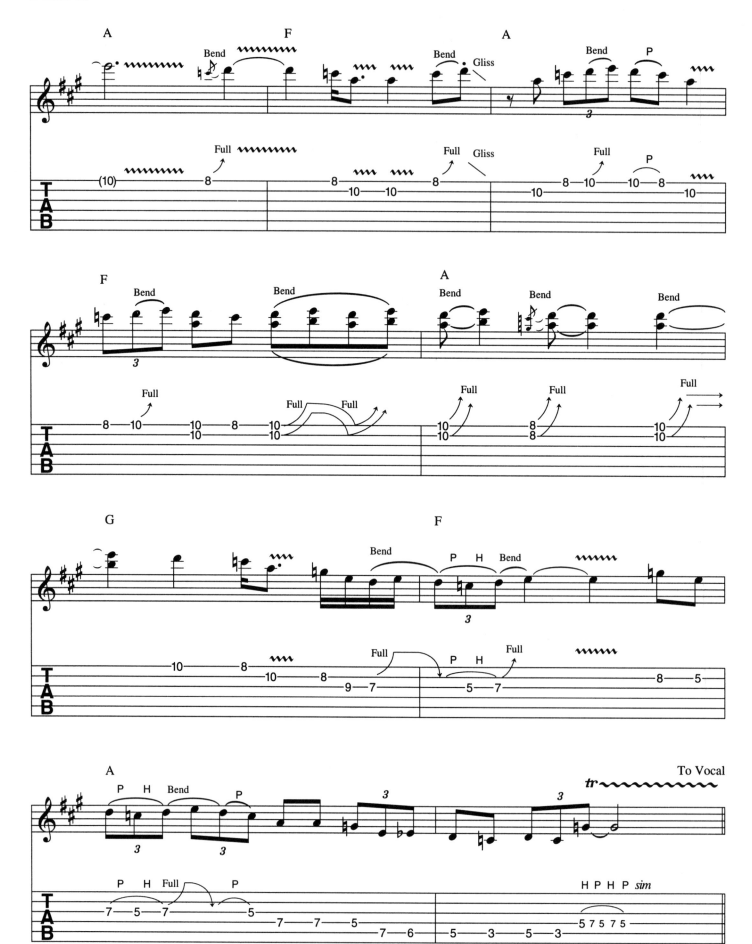

Greeny
Peter Green

CD 'The Blues Guitar Box Vol. 1'
TBB CD 47555/1

By Peter Green

Played on his Les Paul with a mellow jazzy tone, the intro is played at the 8th position with the C major/minor shape with your first finger ½ barré across the 8th fret. The tremolo is played with the first and second fingers on frets 8 and 9 respectively, the 10th fret is covered with the third finger.

Intro

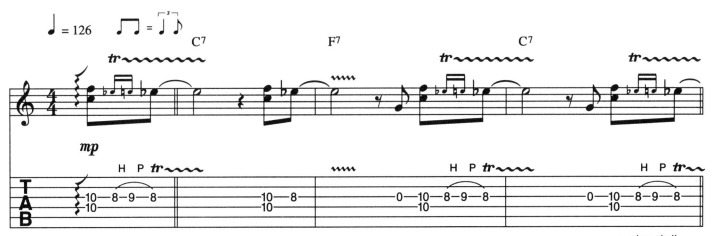

continue simile
through 12 bar sequence.

The first two choruses from this instrumental piece show off Pete Green's playing. His phrasing is full of dynamics which vary even within the bar e.g. bars 10 and 13. Pete's phrases are beautifully sculptured, each one making a statement of its own with the right amount of bend and vibrato added when required. (See over.)

Solo

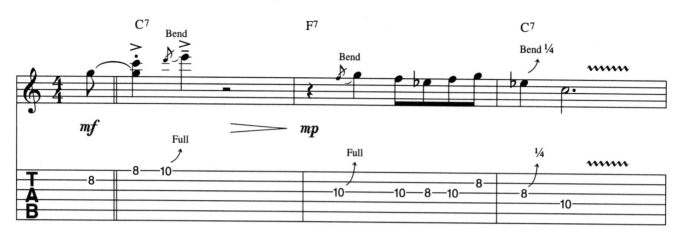

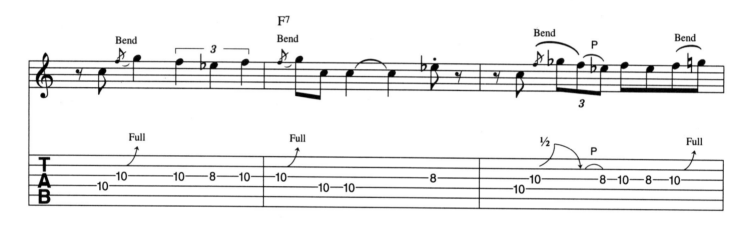

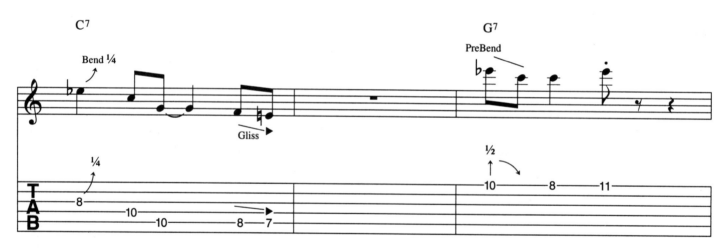

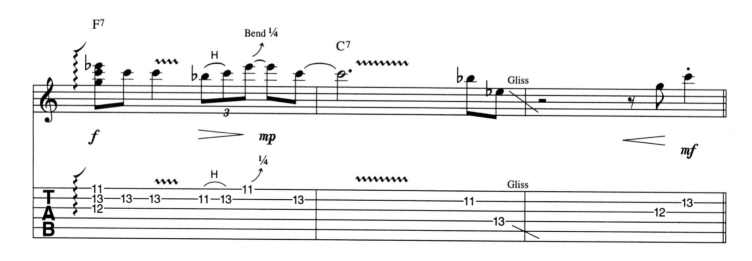

Below is the second chorus which has some great lines e.g. the double stop bends in bar 2 followed by the phrase in bar 3. Playing with the C major and minor pentatonics around the 8th position, the solo ends with the repeated motif in bars 8 – 10.

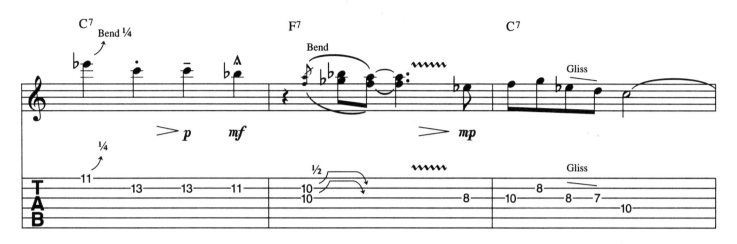

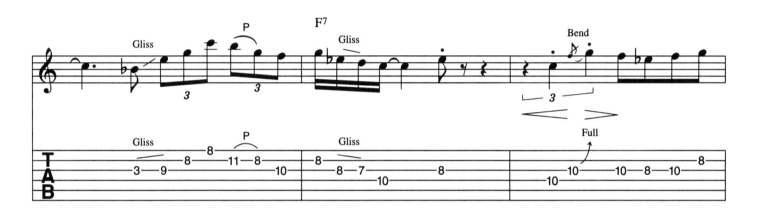

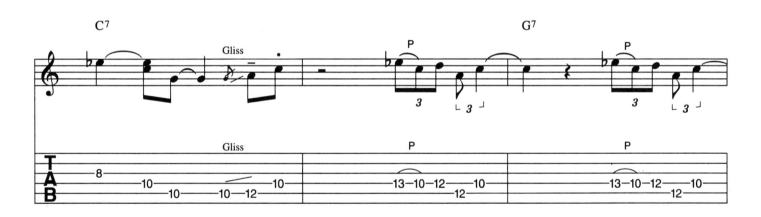

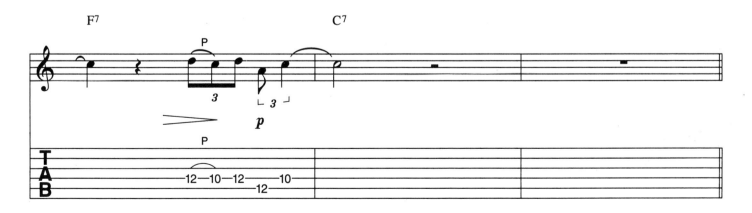

Here's the ending line of the song – C major pentatonic at the 8th position.

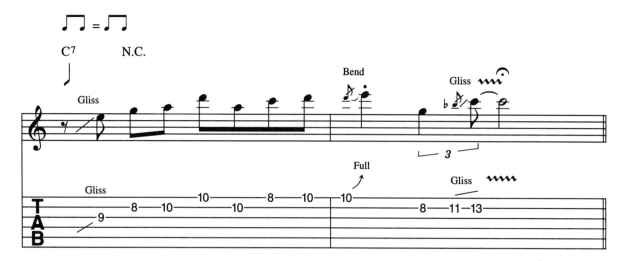

Dimples
John Lee Hooker

CD 'The 20 Blues Greats'
Deja Vu DVCD 2033

Words & Music by James Bracken & John Lee Hooker

John Lee Hooker doesn't always take the solos, often leaving that side of things to another player. However, with this classic song of his he plays the solo line against the riffs which are shown below. These accompanying riffs are played in the open position damping the strings with the palm of your pick hand. There are many variations which should be played rhythmically with feel. John Lee Hooker's whole thing is about playing it your way. Take these ideas and make them work!

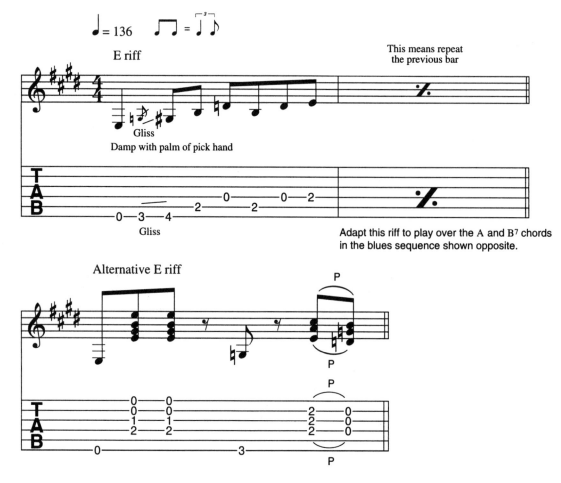

John introduces this ten bar sequence with his classic blues riff played on the 3rd and 4th strings in the open position. Although the bends and pull-offs are notated the way he did it, try your own variations.

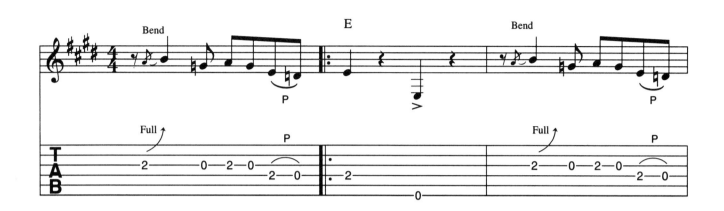

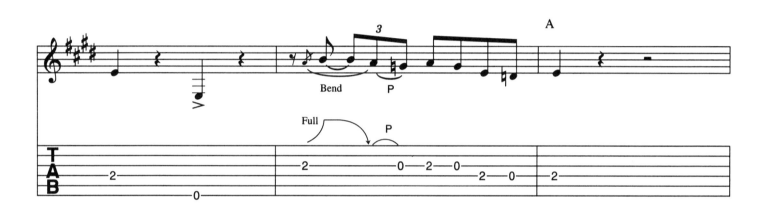

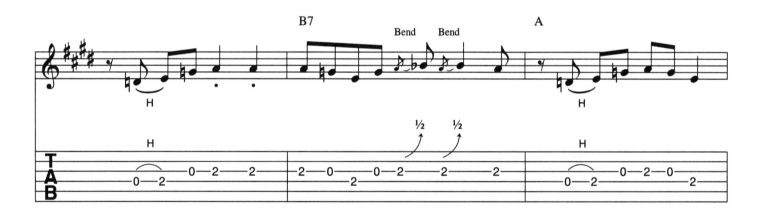

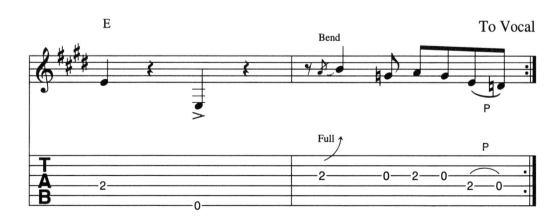

The solo is played over a regular twelve bar sequence. Characteristic of the John Lee Hooker style, it is very percussive, almost like an alternative rhythm part. From bar 2 the double stops are moveable shapes from the 7th to the 10th position with a barré, third finger, across the respective frets. Similar playing to bottleneck style.

Going Down
Freddie King

LP 'Getting Ready'
A&M AMLS 65004

Words & Music by Don Nix

The pulse of this piece is provided by the semiquaver bass line which gives powerful support to Freddie King's 'wired' sound.

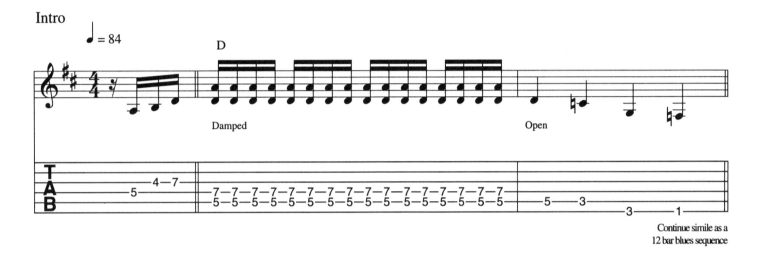

Freddie tears through the song with some great lines. His sound is slightly overdriven to give it an edge and he plays with a great force and vibrato when he hits the string. Here are some of his phrases that he plays between the vocal lines.

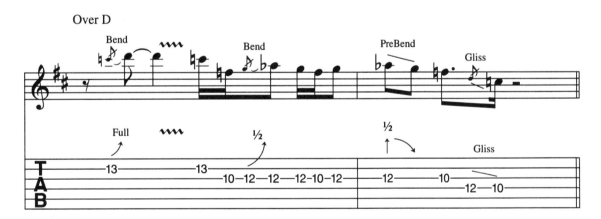

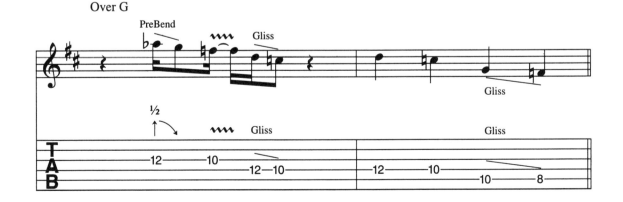

They are all played around the 10th position based upon the Dm blues scale. Notice his timing and the use of pre-bends and pull-offs etc. to play the same idea in different ways.

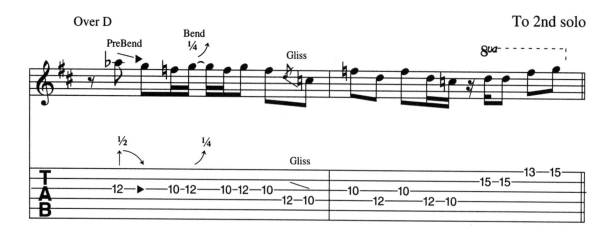

The solo storms in at the 13th position: Freddie's use of 'slow' bends across a beat in bars 2 and 3 for example are very characteristic of his style. Across bars 4 and 7 the phrases are reworked with varying degrees of expression leading to a great answering phrase in bar 8.

Solo

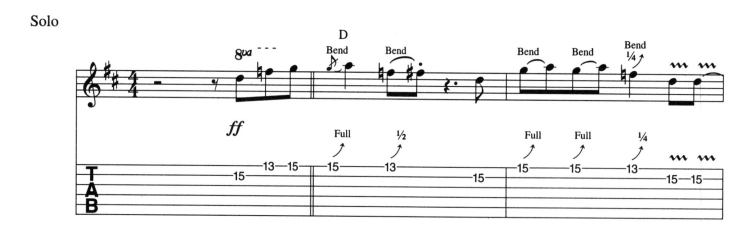

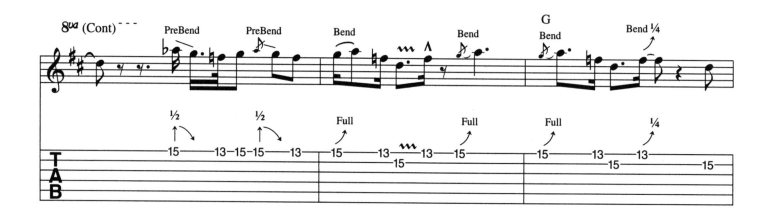

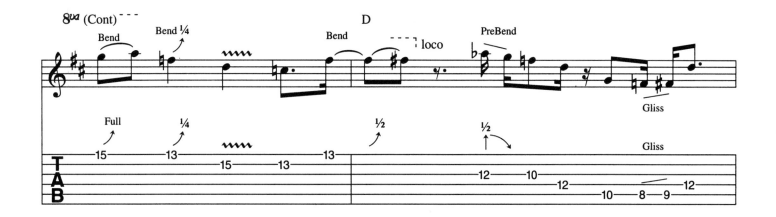

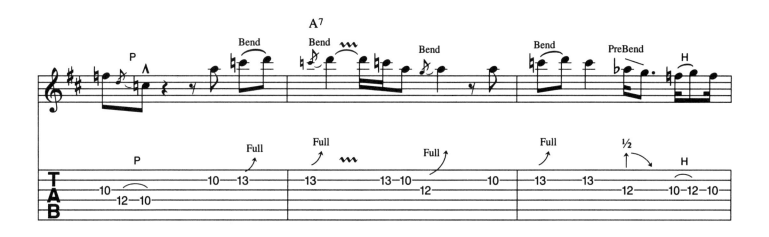

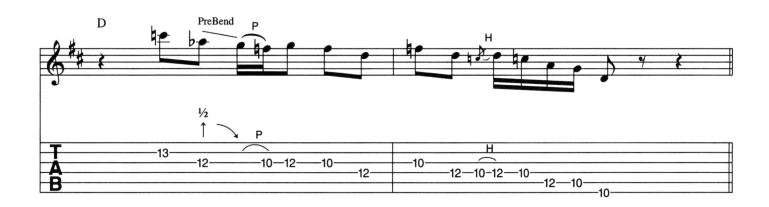

Ice Pick
Albert Collins

LP 'Icepickin''
Sonet SNTF 707A

Words & Music by Albert Collins

The opening riff is played solo and sets the scene for this 'funky' blues. Albert uses a semi-distorted sound for the rhythm at first but then hands it over to his side man who continues it with a clean sound while Albert picks up the tune.

These rhythm patterns should be interpreted very percussively.

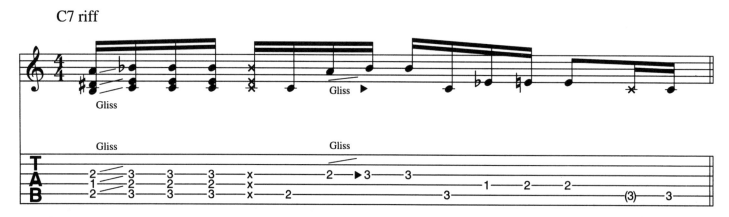

C7 riff

Move pattern to 6th position for F^7
and 8th position for the G^7 in the
12 bar blues sequence

Bars 1 and 2 of the theme that follows are played with a sax section either answering or playing octave unison with the guitar. Albert answers this line in bars 3 and 4 with a simple line but the vibrato added to the note gives the edge to his sound. A similar pattern continues over the F^7 and G^7 bars of the blues sequence before finishing on a great Cm pentatonic turnaround line starting with a bend on the 13th fret but then moving down to the 8th position.

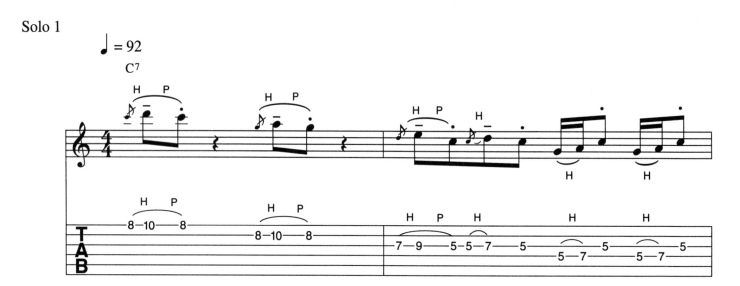

Solo 1

♩ = 92

C^7

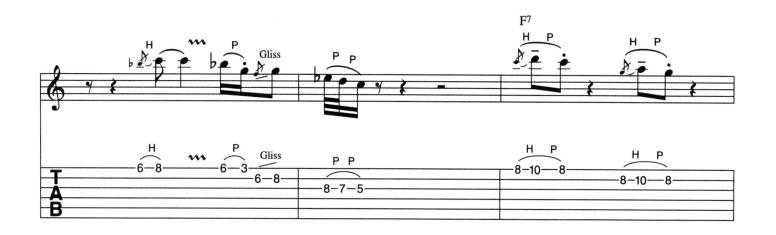

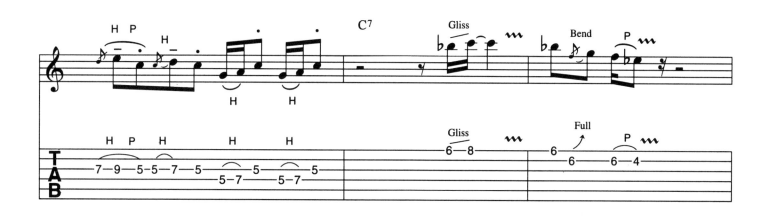

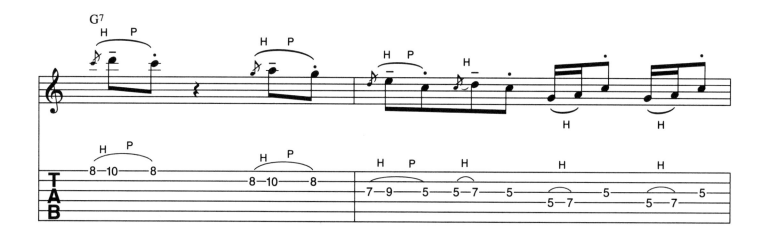

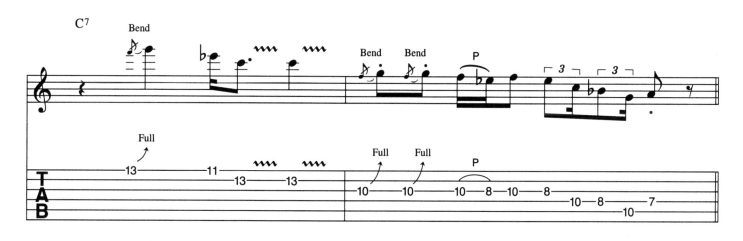

Albert's solo then continues over C⁷ – here are a few ideas. They are based around the Cm pentatonic at the 8th position. Note his use of pull-offs and ¼ tone bends to give a sense of urgency to the phrase.

Solo 2

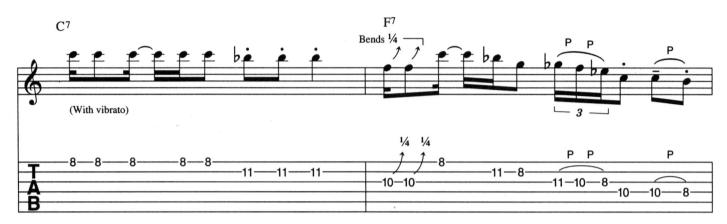

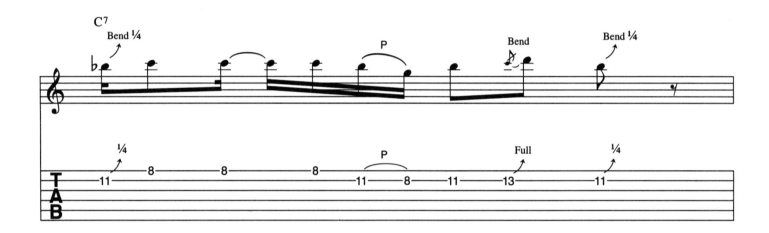

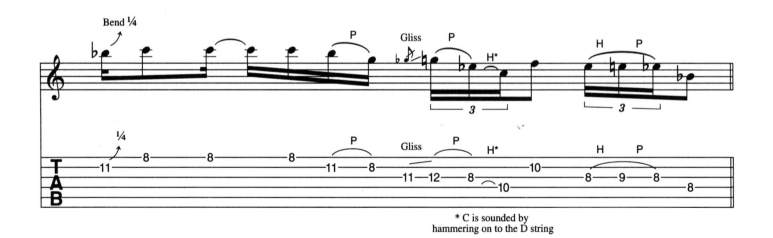

* C is sounded by
hammering on to the D string

All Your Love (I Miss Loving)

Gary Moore

CD 'Still Got The Blues'
Virgin CDV 2612

Words & Music by Otis Rush

Gary uses a heavily sustained sound throughout the piece. This famous opening line using bends and pull-offs to great effect is based around Am pentatonic. The opening gliss up to top A, although marked to begin on D, is open to interpretation. In bars 4 and 8 the harmonic as well as the note is played; sustain and reverberation highlight the effect.

The following 3 accompanying riffs are played under the vocal in the blues sequence.

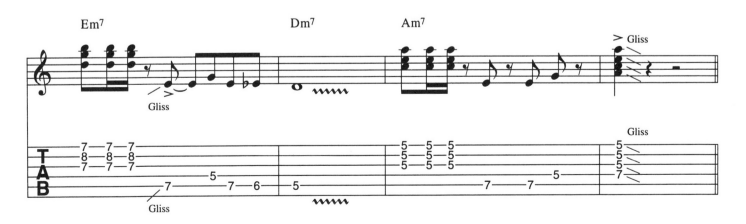

Intro

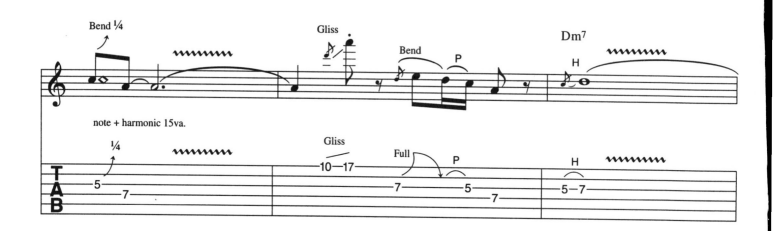

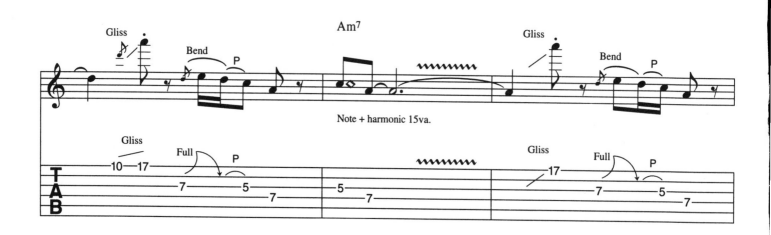

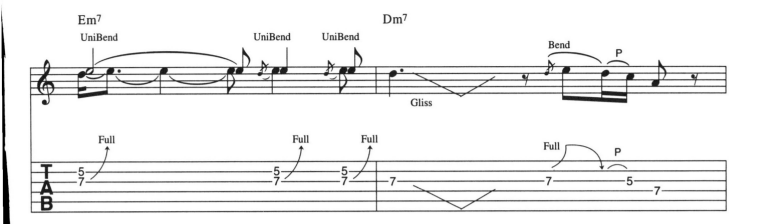

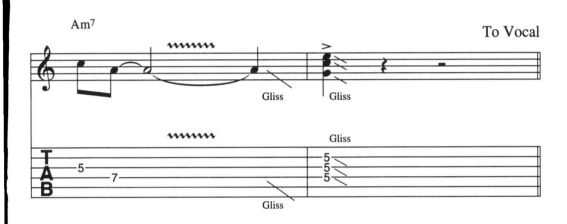

The first 12 bars of the solo section on page 44 are the same as Clapton's original version from 1966. In the pick up bar the A played on the 2nd string is sustained while playing the C each time, indicated by the tied notes. The solo really picks up steam into **B** with a long slow bend from the bar before. The phrase in bars 2 and 3 requires a very smooth hammer on/pull-off technique. Gary's flawless execution of this really moves the piece along at this point. He breaks from the fast runs to return to another characteristically expressive bend in bar 5 while picking out the harmonics in bars 6 and 7.

Solo

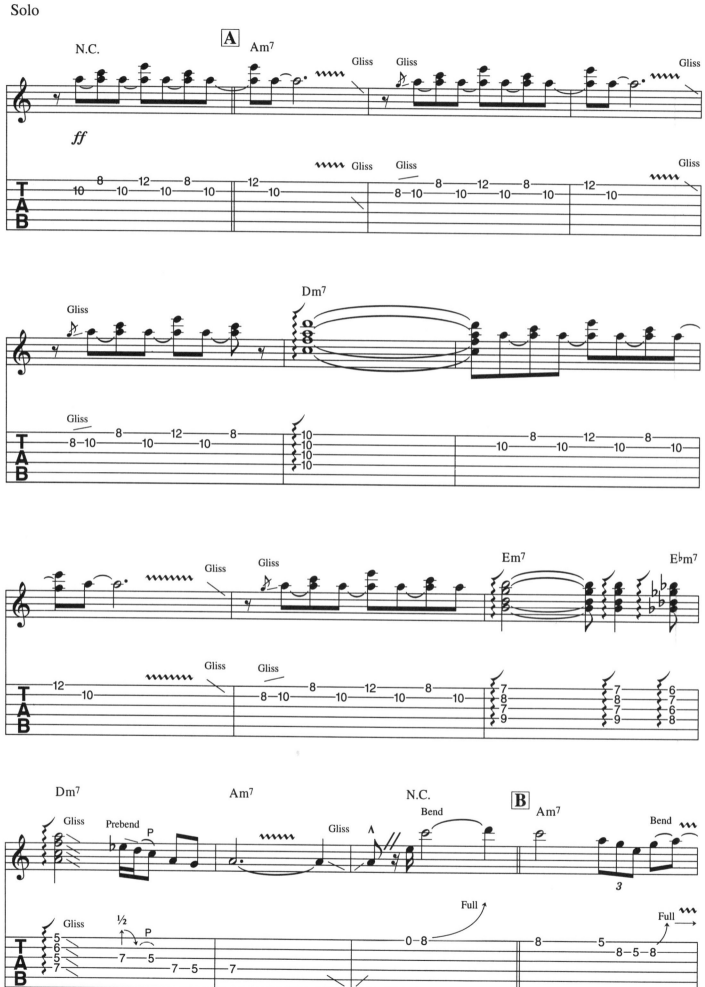

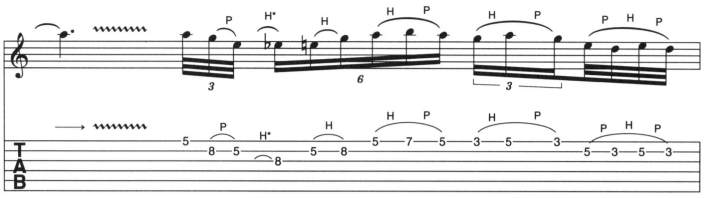

* Note is sounded by hammering-on action
but not from a preceding note

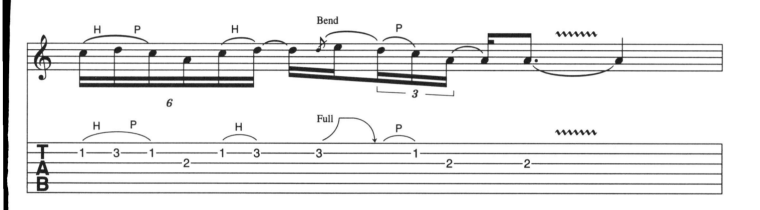

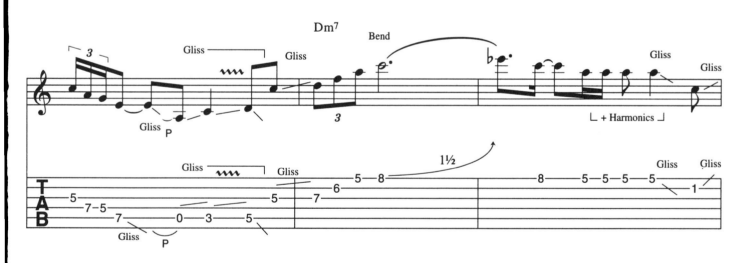

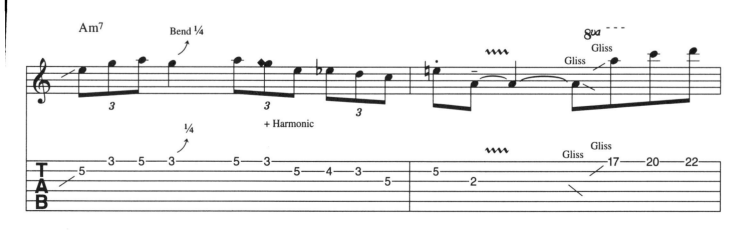

Intro

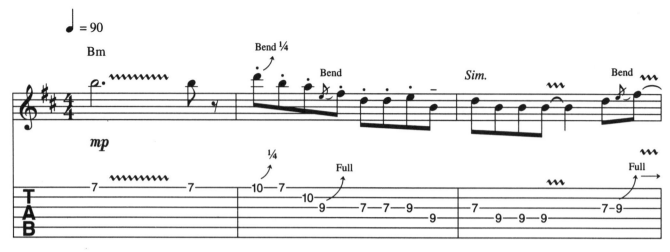

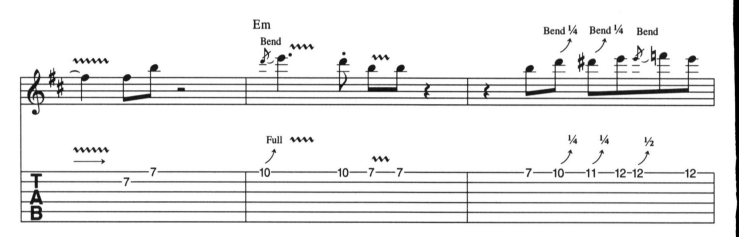

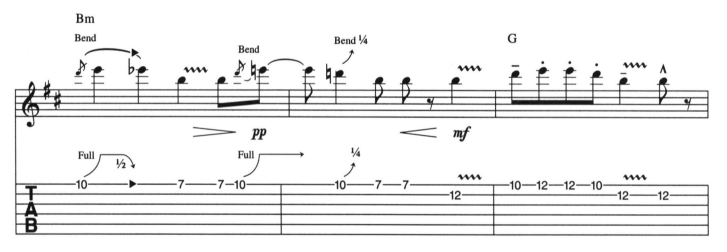

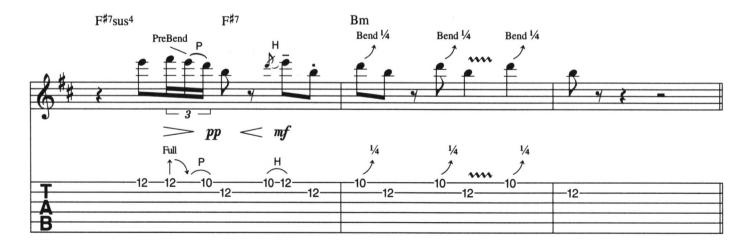

47

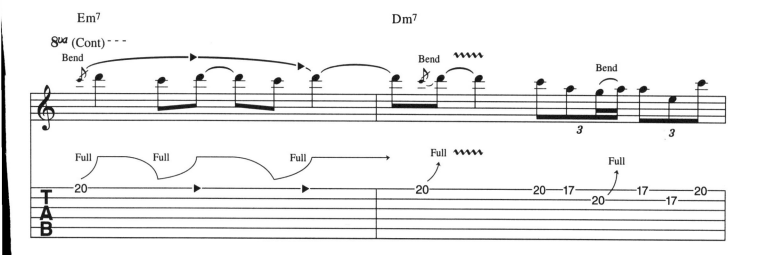

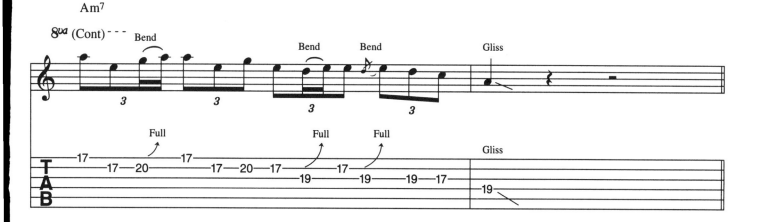

The Thrill Is Gone
B.B. King

CD 'Q The Blues'
Polygram AH LCD 1

Words & Music by Roy Hawkins & Rick Darnell

'The Thrill Is Gone' is probably B.B. King's biggest hit, written in 1951. B.B. plays this slow blues so delicately and soulfully it cries out. The notes are played so quietly but the occasional phrase is accented so it really speaks out. For example, in bar 7 the notes are first played *pp* then in bar 8 they speak out *mf*. The following intro is accompanied by rhythm section only, while the 2nd verse onwards includes string orchestra.

This first solo is again expressive. Note the *pp* in bar 5 and the sudden accents in bar 6. His Bm pentatonic lines will provide you with enough ideas and inspiration to take you through any minor blues.